Better Guitar Wit'

Rockschool

www.rockschool.co.uk

Welcome To Guitar Grade 6

Welcome to the Rockschool Guitar Grade 6 pack. The book and CD contain everything needed to play guitar in this grade. In the book you will find the exam scores in both standard guitar notation and TAB. The accompanying CD has full stereo mixes of each tune, backing tracks to play along with for practice, tuning notes and spoken two bar count-ins to each piece. Handy tips on playing the pieces and the marking schemes can be found in the Guru's Guide on page 26. If you have any queries about this or any other Rockschool exam, please call us on **0845 460 4747**, email us at *info@rockschool.co.uk* or visit our website *www.rockschool.co.uk*. Good luck!

Level 3 Requirements for Grades 6, 7 & 8

The nine Rockschool grades are divided into four levels. These levels correspond to the levels of the National Qualifications Framework (NQF). Further details about the NQF can be found at *www.qca.org.uk/NQF*. Details of all Rockschool's accredited qualifications can be found at *www.qca.org.uk/openquals*.

Guitar Grade 6 is part of Level 3. This Level is for those of you who wish to stretch and refine all aspects of your playing at an advanced level of technique and musical expression.

Grade 6: in this grade you are developing the confidence of the advanced player across the range of physical and expressive techniques. You will start experimenting with a range of techniques across a number of musical styles. There is a greater emphasis on personal expression and you will display your own musical personality through ad libbing and soloing.

Grade 7: in this grade you are now confident in your abilities across the range of physical and expressive techniques. You will be experimenting with a range of these techniques across a number of styles. You will also be comfortable with a range of rhythms and time signatures other than common time. Your solos will be musically expressive and you will have the confidence to apply modal ideas in a number of soloing contexts.

Grade 8: you will play effortlessly with a wide range of physical and expressive techniques at your command. You will be able to use these at will across a range of styles and musical contexts. You will be comfortable playing pieces employing a number of different time signatures (including changes from bar to bar) and you will display mastery of a number of musical styles. Your solos will be highly musical and employ techniques across the range. You will also be highly sensitive to all aspects of musical presentation.

Guitar Exams at Grade 6

There are **two** types of exam that can be taken using this pack: a Grade Exam and a Performance Certificate.

Guitar Grade 6 Exam: this is for players who want to develop performance and technical skills

Players wishing to enter for a Guitar Grade 6 exam need to prepare **three** pieces of which **one** may be a free choice piece chosen from outside the printed repertoire. In addition you must prepare the technical exercises in the book, undertake quick study piece, take an ear test and answer general musicianship questions. Samples of these tests are printed in the book along with audio examples on the CD.

Guitar Grade 6 Performance Certificate: this is for players who want to focus on performing in a range of styles

To enter for your Guitar Grade 6 Performance Certificate you play pieces only. You can choose any **five** of the six tunes printed in this book, or you can choose to bring in up to **two** free choice pieces as long as they meet the standards set out by Rockschool. Free choice piece checklists for all grades can be found on the Rockschool website: *www.rockschool.co.uk*.

Guitar Notation Explained

THE MUSICAL STAVE shows pitches and rhythms and is divided by lines into bars. Pitches are named after the first seven letters of the alphabet.

TABLATURE graphically represents the guitar fingerboard. Each horizontal line represents a string, and each number represents a fret.

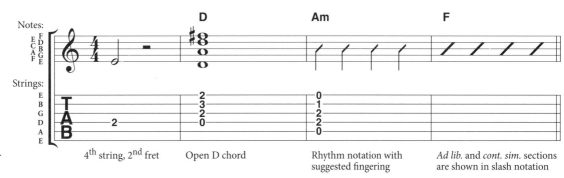

4th string, 2nd fret | Open D chord | Rhythm notation with suggested fingering | Ad lib. and cont. sim. sections are shown in slash notation

Definitions For Special Guitar Notation

HAMMER ON: Pick the lower note, then sound the higher note by fretting it without picking.

PULL OFF: Pick the higher note then sound the lower note by lifting the finger without picking.

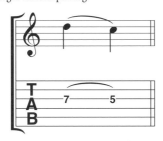

SLIDE: Pick the first note, then slide to the next with the same finger.

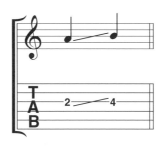

STRING BENDS: Pick the first note then bend (or release the bend) to the pitch indicated in brackets.

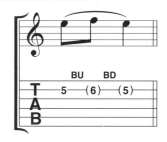

GLISSANDO: A small slide off of a note toward the end of its rhythmic duration. Do not slide 'into' the following note – subsequent notes should be repicked.

VIBRATO: Vibrate the note by bending and releasing the string smoothly and continuously.

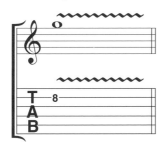

TRILL: Rapidly alternate between the two bracketed notes by hammering on and pulling off.

NATURAL HARMONICS: Lightly touch the string above the indicated fret then pick to sound a harmonic.

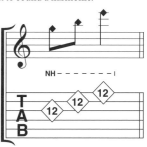

PINCHED HARMONICS: Bring the thumb of the picking hand into contact with the string immediately after the pick.

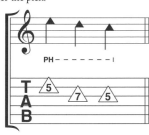

PICK HAND TAP: Strike the indicated note with a finger from the picking hand. Usually followed by a pull off.

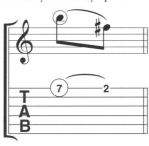

FRET HAND TAP: As pick hand tap, but use fretting hand. Usually followed by a pull off or hammer on.

QUARTER TONE BEND: Pick the note indicated and bend the string up by a quarter tone.

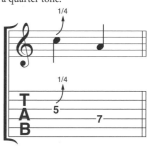

PRE-BENDS: Before picking the note, bend the string from the fret indicated between the staves, to the equivalent pitch indicated in brackets in the TAB

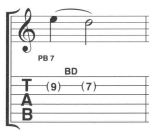

WHAMMY BAR BEND: Use the whammy bar to bend notes to the pitches indicated in brackets in the TAB

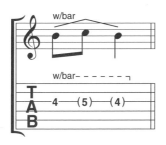

D.%. al Coda

D.C. al Fine

- Go back to the sign (%), then play until the bar marked *To Coda* ⊕ then skip to the section marked ⊕ *Coda*.

- Go back to the beginning of the song and play until the bar marked *Fine* (end).

- Repeat bars between signs.

- When a repeated section has different endings, play the first ending only the first time and the second ending only the second time.

Big Big Big

Simon Troup

† All palm muting is very light

© 2006 rock School Ltd.

This music is copyright. Photocopying is illegal.

© 2006 Rock School Ltd.

This music is copyright. Photocopying is illegal.

PMA

Jimi Savage

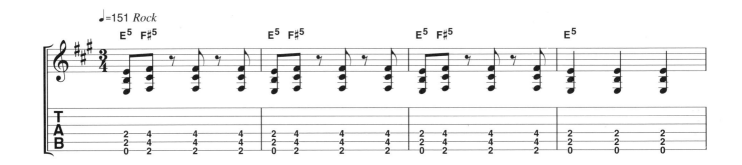

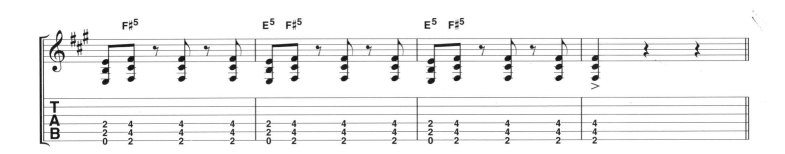

† Bend note and hold, dip bar a semitone and return

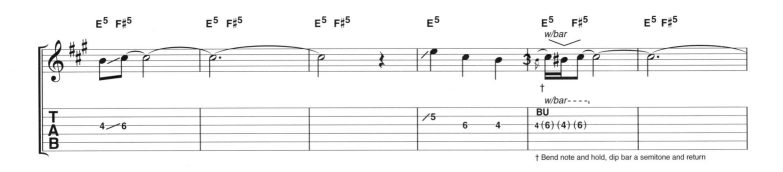

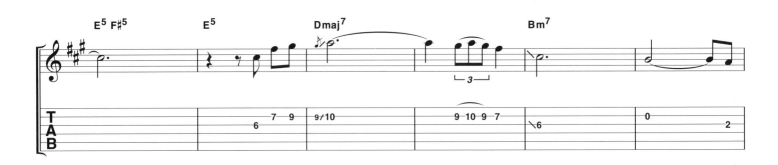

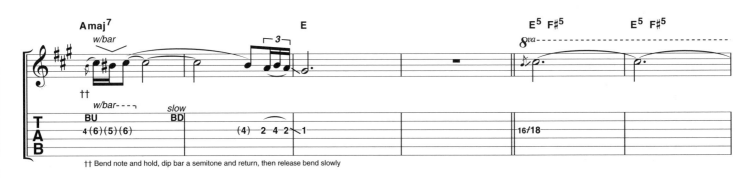

†† Bend note and hold, dip bar a semitone and return, then release bend slowly

© 2006 Rock School Ltd.

This music is copyright. Photocopying is illegal.

© 2006 Rock School Ltd.

This music is copyright. Photocopying is illegal.

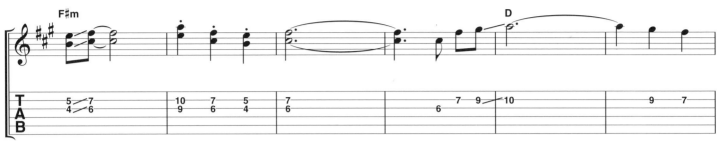

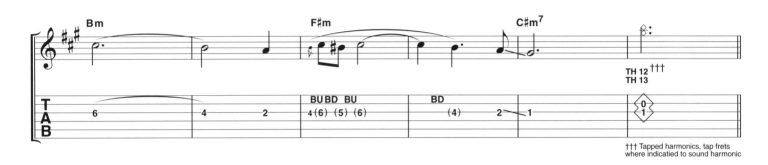

††† Tapped harmonics, tap frets
where indicatied to sound harmonic

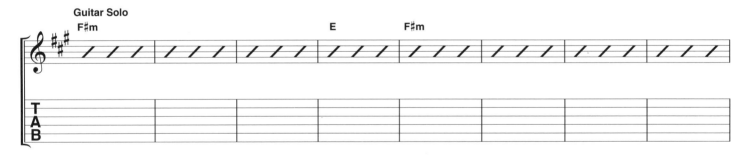

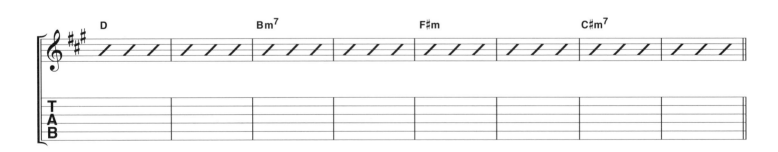

© 2006 Rock School Ltd.

This music is copyright. Photocopying is illegal.

© 2006 rock School Ltd.

This music is copyright. Photocopying is illegal.

Mud Pie

Hussein Boon

Guitar Grade 6

© 2006 Rock School Ltd.

This music is copyright. Photocopying is illegal.

© 2006 rock School Ltd.

This music is copyright. Photocopying is illegal.

Musement Park

Deirdre Cartwright

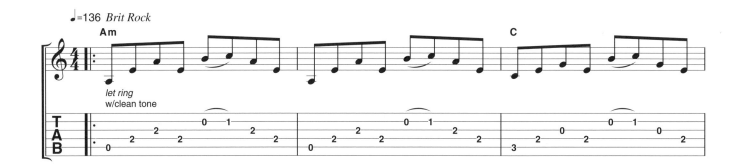

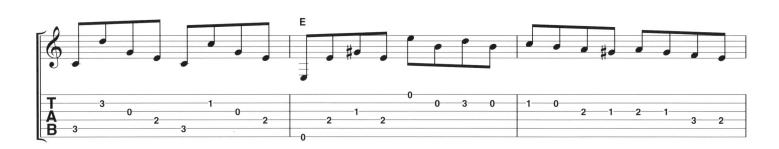

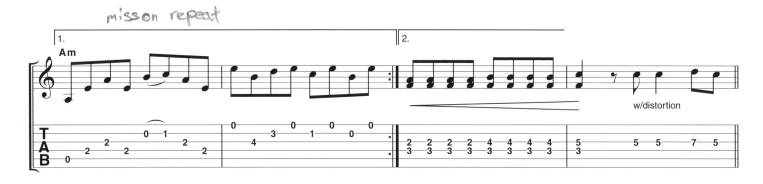

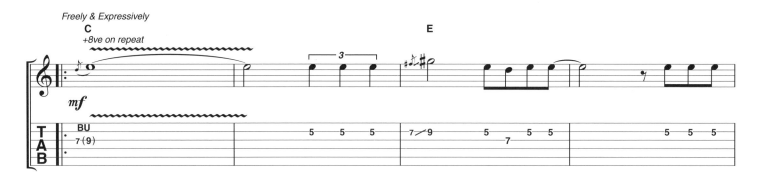

© 2006 Rock School Ltd.

This music is copyright. Photocopying is illegal.

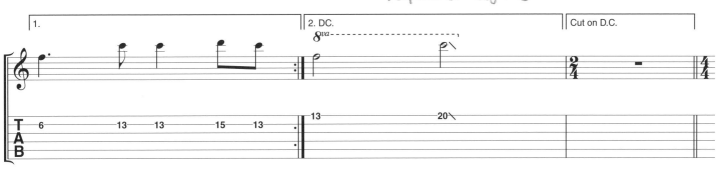

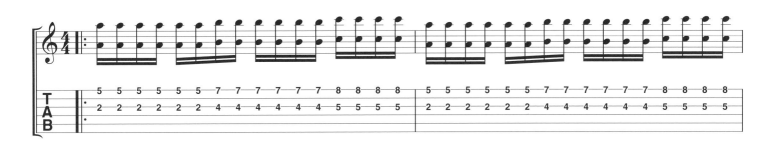

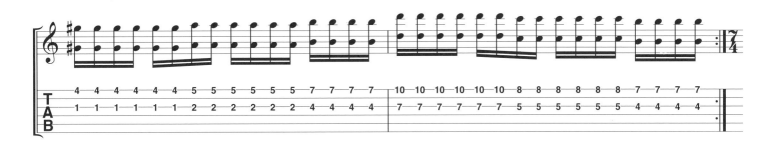

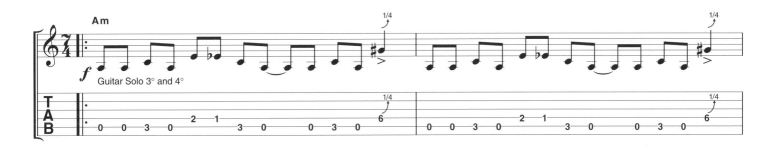

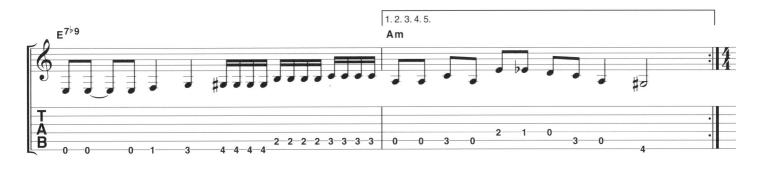

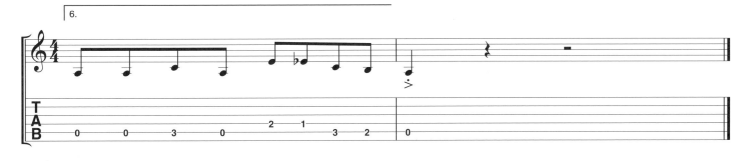

© 2006 Rock School Ltd.

This music is copyright. Photocopying is illegal.

One By One

Noam Lederman & James Creed

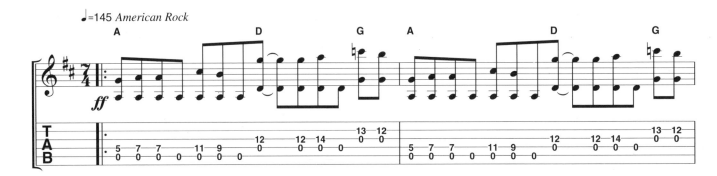

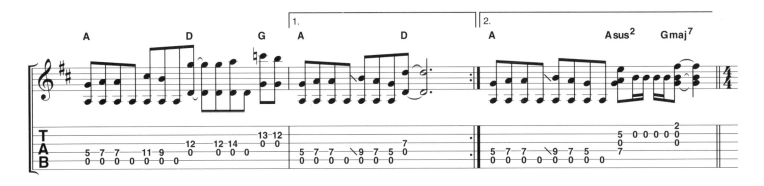

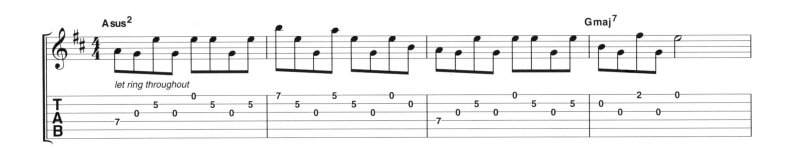

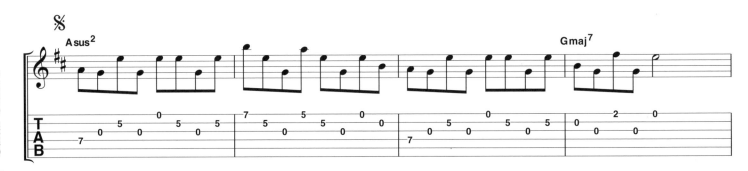

© 2006 Rock School Ltd.

Guitar Grade 6

This music is copyright. Photocopying is illegal.

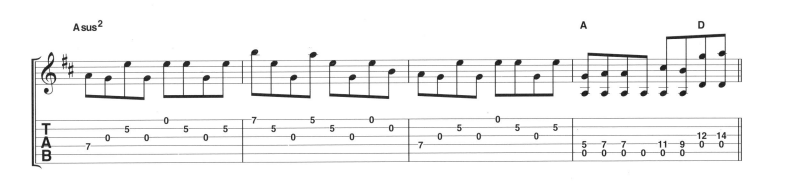

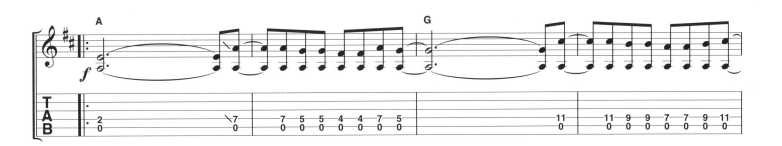

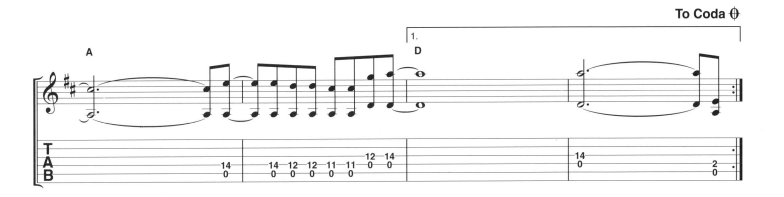

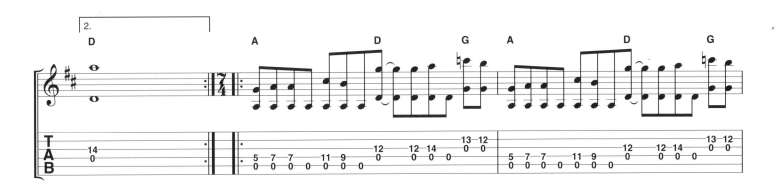

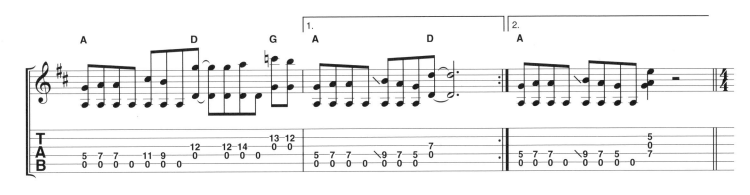

© 2006 Rock School Ltd.

This music is copyright. Photocopying is illegal.

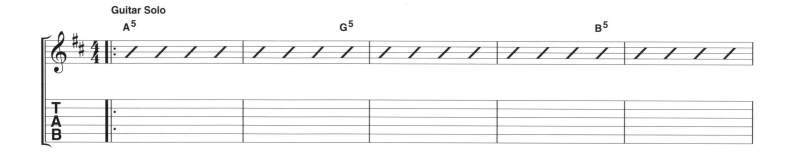

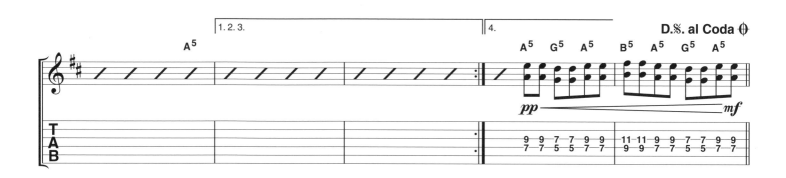

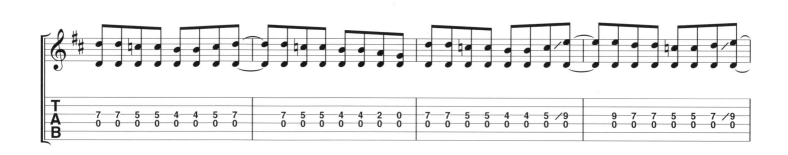

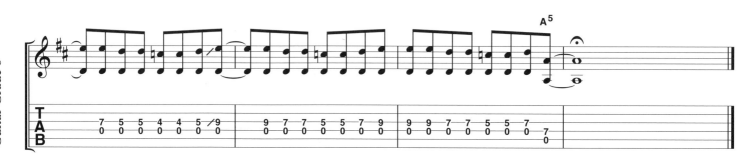

© 2006 Rock School Ltd.

This music is copyright. Photocopying is illegal.

Guitar Grade 6

September Chill

John Parricelli

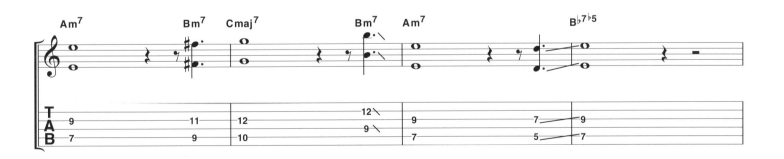

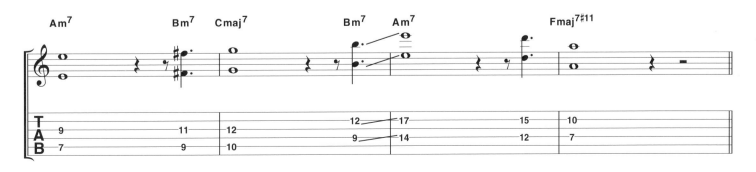

© 2006 Rock School Ltd.

This music is copyright. Photocopying is illegal.

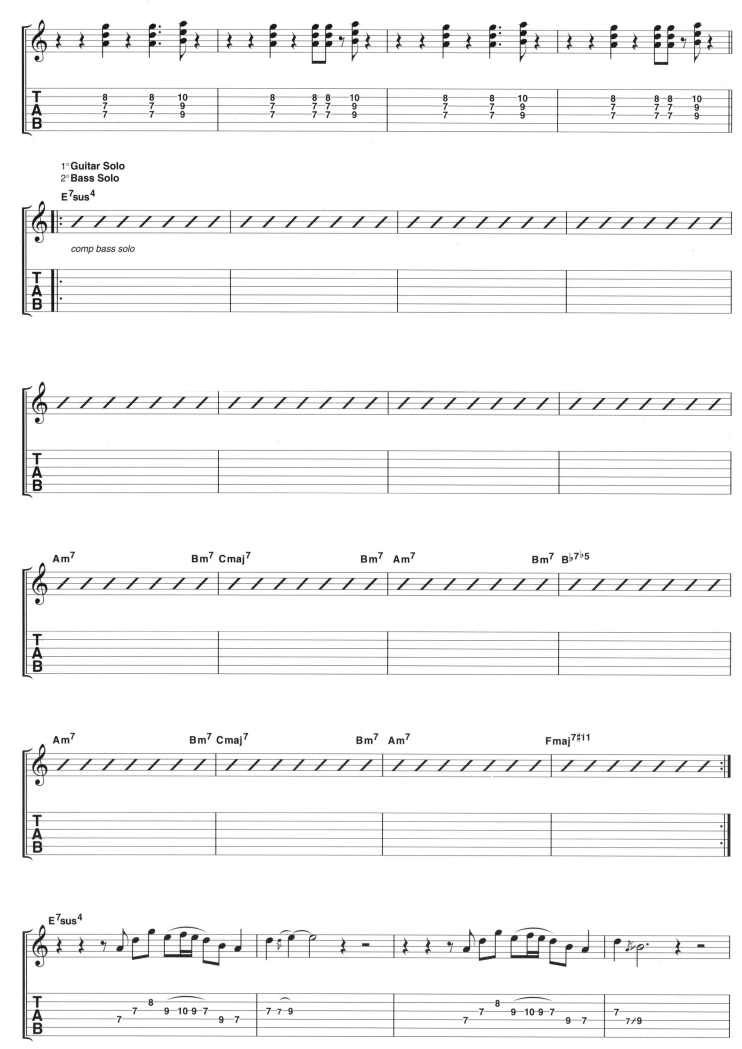

© 2006 Rock School Ltd.

This music is copyright. Photocopying is illegal.

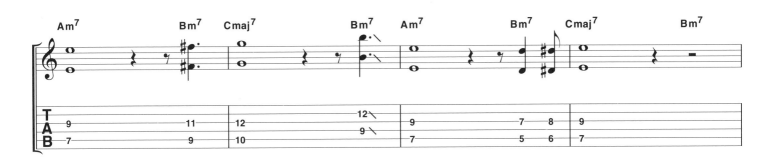

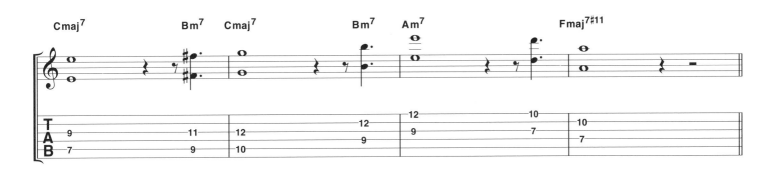

2° Develop part

© 2006 Rock School Ltd.

This music is copyright. Photocopying is illegal.

Technical Exercises

In this section, the examiner will ask you to play a selection of exercises drawn from each of the three groups shown below. Groups A and B contain examples of the kinds of scales/modes and arpeggios you can use when playing the pieces. Group C contains a chord study. In Group D you will be asked to prepare the exercise shown and play it to the CD backing track. You do not need to memorise the exercises (and can use the book in the exam) but the examiner will be looking for the speed of your response. The examiner will also give credit for the level of your musicality.

Groups A and B should be prepared in the following keys: chromatically from G–B and all have their root note on the 6th string. The modes should be played as two consecutive scales: Ionian/Dorian or Dorian/Phrygian. Groups A, B and C should be played at ♩ = 60. The examiner will give you this tempo in the exam.

Group A: Scales & Modes

1. Ionian mode. G Ionian mode shown.

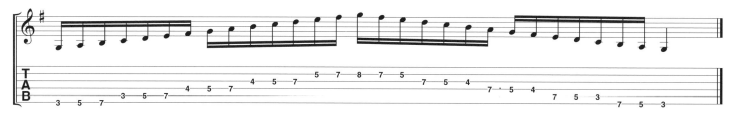

2. Dorian mode. A dorian mode shown.

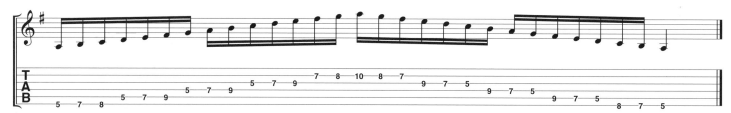

3. Phrygian mode. B phrygian mode shown.

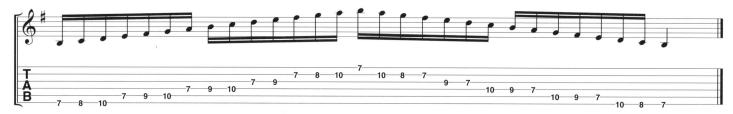

4. Diminished scales. A diminished scale shown.

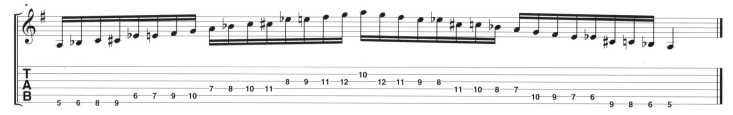

5. Harmonic minor scale. B♭ harmonic minor scale shown

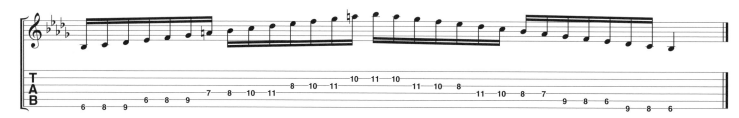

Group B: Arpeggios

1. Major ^{7} arpeggios. G major ^{7} arpeggio shown.

2. Minor $^{7\flat5}$ arpeggios. A minor $^{7\flat5}$ arpeggio shown.

3. Diminished ^{7} arpeggios. B diminished ^{7} arpeggio shown.

4. Dominant ^{7} triplet arpeggios. A dominant ^{7} triplet arpeggio shown.

Group C: Chords

In the exam you will be asked to play one of the chord sequences shown below.

1. Sequence 1. Prepare in the keys G–B

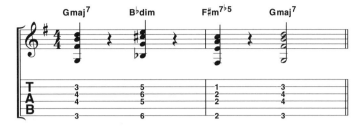

2. Sequence 2. Prepare in the keys C–E

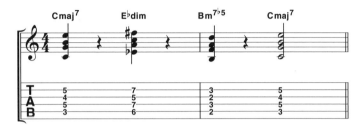

Group D: Tapping Study

In the exam you will be asked to play the following tapping study to the CD backing track.   The tempo is $\quarternote = 100$.

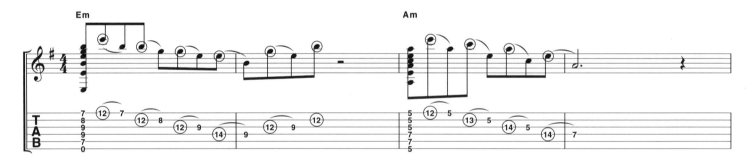

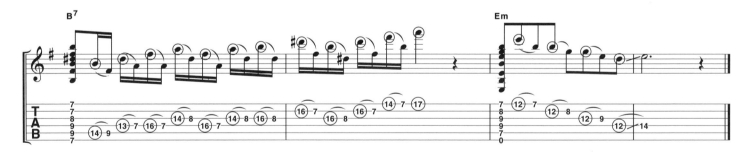

Quick Study Piece

At this grade you will be asked to prepare a short Quick Study Piece (QSP) which will be given for you to prepare with audio 20 minutes before entering the exam room. You should be prepared to play a QSP in any of the following styles: blues, rock, funk or jazz. The QSP is in the form of a lead sheet and it is up to you to create your own interpretation of the music, particularly where you have to compose and perform your own part. You will then perform the piece to a backing track in the exam.

The QSP will be in standard notation and TAB and you are required to master your version of the piece within the time given. Printed below is an example of the type of QSP you are likely to receive in the exam. The CD contains an idealised version and a backing track.

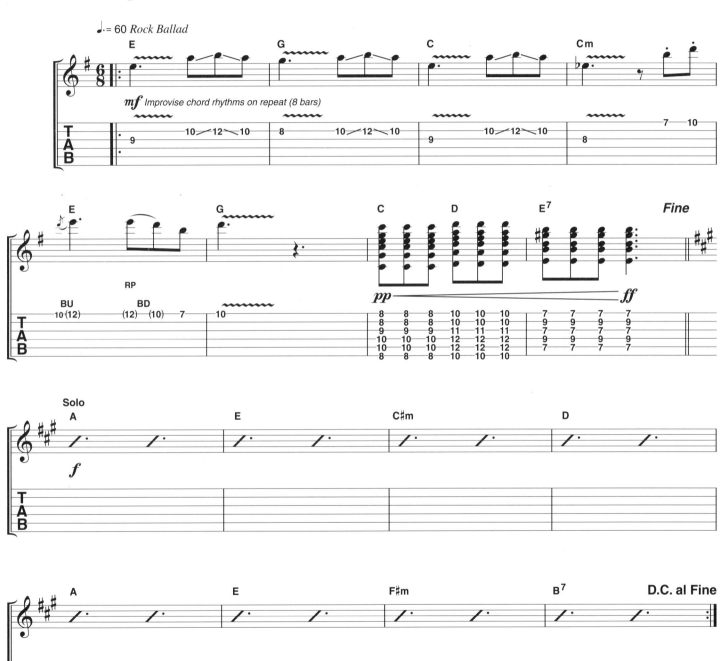

Ear Tests

There are two ear tests in this grade. The examiner will play each test to you twice on CD. You will find one example of each type of test you will be given in the exam printed below.

Test 1: Melodic Recall

You will be asked to play back on your guitar a melody of not more than four bars composed from either the G, A or B ionian mode. The test may include hammer-ons, pull-offs, vibrato, slides and bends with vibrato. You will be given the tonic note and you will hear the test twice with a drum and bass backing. There will be a short break for you to practise the test and then the test will recommence. You will play the melody with the drum backing. This test is continuous. The tempo is ♩ = 80.

Test 2: Chord and Rhythm Recall

You will be asked to play back a four bar rhythmic chord progression on your guitar. You will be told the tonic chord and hear the rhythmic chord progression played twice with a drum backing. There will then be a short break for you to practise and then the test will recommence. You will play the rhythmic chord progression with the drum backing. This test is continuous. The tempo is ♩ = 80.

General Musicianship Questions

You will be asked five General Musicianship Questions at the end of the exam. The examiner will ask questions based on a pieces or pieces you have played in the exam. Some of the theoretical topics can be found in the Technical Exercises.

Topics:

i) Music theory
ii) Knowledge of your instrument

The music theory questions will cover the following topics at this grade:

> Knowledge of all music signs as displayed on the staff

Knowledge of the construction of the following scales and arpeggios:

> Modes of the major scale: dorian & phrygian
> Harmonic minor scale
> Diminished scale
> Major ^{7} arpeggios
> Diminished arpeggios
> Minor $^{7\flat5}$ arpeggios

The instrument knowledge questions will cover the following topics at this grade:

> All aspects of guitar construction
> Recognition of main guitar makes
> Recognition of main guitar amplifiers
> Use of appropriate tone and volume controls for different styles

Questions on all these topics will be based on pieces played by you in the exam. Tips on how to approach this part of the exams can be found in the Rockschool Companion Guide and on the Rockschool website: *www.rockschool.co.uk*.

The Guru's Guide To Guitar Grade 6

This section contains some handy hints compiled by Rockschool's Guitar Guru to help you get the most out of the performance pieces. Do feel free to adapt the tunes to suit your playing style. Remember, these tunes are your chance to show your musical imagination and personality.

The TAB fingerings are suggestions only. Feel free to use different neck positions as they suit you. Please also note that any solos featured in the full mixes are not meant to be indicative of the standard required for the grade.

Guitar Grade 6 Tunes

Rockschool tunes help you play the hit tunes you enjoy. The pieces have been written by top pop and rock composers and players according to style specifications drawn up by Rockschool.

The tunes printed here fall into two categories. The first category can be called the 'contemporary mainstream' and features current styles in today's charts. The second category of pieces consists of 'roots styles', those classic grooves and genres which influence every generation of performers.

CD full mix track 1, backing track 8: Big Big Big

A Latin track in the style of Carlos Santana. This piece requires considerable control to pull off on account of the sparse nature of the backing track which leaves no room for error. The initial guitar figure is played with a palm mute and the bends need to be crisp and accurate. You will need a degree of overdrive but not too dirty, enough to allow notes to sustain, a Santana trademark. The solo gives you the opportunity to show off the harmonic minor scale.

Composer: Simon Troup.

CD full mix track 2, backing track 9: PMA

In the early 1990s, guitar heroes were all the rage and players such as Joe Satriani, Steve Vai and Eric Johnson held sway. This track takes many elements from their playing. The song itself mixes a driving hard rock opening with the more lyrical melodic playing that players such as Vai and Johnson are famous for. You need to play this with a degree of sensitivity, particularly in the middle sections, where the main theme is restated but more tenderly. Nevertheless, the rock sections need power and great deal of control, as well as technical ability, to pull off.

Composer: Jimi Savage

CD full mix track 3, backing track 10: Mud Pie

Back by popular demand, we have put Mud Pie, a staple from the RS2K syllabus in Grade 5, into this syllabus at the Grade that, with hindsight, it ought to have been in. This barnstorming southern boogie track, typical of players such as Stevie Ray Vaughan, is played more or less as it was before, the only exception being the extended solo section to bring it in line with the other tracks in this grade. The performance will need the chops and plenty of confidence to bring off.

Composer: Hussein Boon.

CD full mix track 4, backing track 11: Musement Park

A rock piece that showcases the modern way of writing songs: a quiet opening section picked with or without a plectrum that is in a more understated mood than the bravura, overdriven guitar part that follows. This is repeated before moving into an irregular time signature section that really drives the piece forward and where the emphasis is on picking hand accuracy and technique. You should be looking really to rip in the closing sections.

Composer: Deirdre Cartwright

CD full mix track 5, backing track 12: One By One

Nirvana revolutionised popular music in the early 1990s with their fusion of heavy metal and punk: grunge was born. This is a fast-paced, guitar work out played loud. The opening section is played in double stops in 7/4 time. The main section is arpeggio based. The structure is quite repetitive, so feel free to develop the part in the repeated sections and in the reprises. Let rip in the guitar solo section.

Composers: Noam Lederman & James Creed.

CD full mix track 6, backing track 13: September Chill

This funk fusion piece is evocative of players such as Pat Metheney or John Scofield. You should aim for a limpid tone and be comfortable with the stabbed chords and the melody line which needs control and accuracy. Much of the performance will be taken up with trying to create the right sort of mood, a matter of feel as much as of technique.

Composer: John Parricelli.

CD Musicians:

Guitars: Deirdre Cartwright; John Parricelli; Jimi Savage; Keith Airey; Hussein Boon
Bass: Henry Thomas
Drums: Noam Lederman
Keyboards and programming: Alastair Gavin

Guitar Grade 6 Marking Schemes

The table below shows the marking scheme for the Guitar Grade 6 exam.

ELEMENT	PASS	MERIT	DISTINCTION
Piece 1	13 out of 20	15 out of 20	17+ out of 20
Piece 2	13 out of 20	15 out of 20	17+ out of 20
Piece 3	13 out of 20	15 out of 20	17+ out of 20
Technical Exercises	6 out of 10	7–8 out of 10	9+ out of 10
Quick Study Piece	11 out of 15	12–13 out of 15	14+ out of 15
Ear Tests	6 out of 10	7–8 out of 10	9+ out of 10
General Musicianship Questions	3 out of 5	4 out of 5	5 out of 5
Total Marks	**Pass: 65%+**	**Merit: 75%+**	**Distinction: 85%+**

The table below shows the markings scheme for the Guitar Grade 6 Performance Certificate.

ELEMENT	PASS	MERIT	DISTINCTION
Piece 1	14 out of 20	16 out of 20	18+ out of 20
Piece 2	14 out of 20	16 out of 20	18+ out of 20
Piece 3	14 out of 20	16 out of 20	18+ out of 20
Piece 4	14 out of 20	16 out of 20	18+ out of 20
Piece 5	14 out of 20	16 out of 20	18+ out of 20
Total Marks	**Pass: 70%+**	**Merit: 80%+**	**Distinction: 90%+**

Entering Rockschool Exams

Entering a Rockschool exam is easy. Please read through these instructions carefully before filling in the exam entry form. Information on current exam fees can be obtained from Rockschool by ringing 0845 460 4747 or by logging on to our website *www.rockschool.co.uk.*

• You should enter for your exam when you feel ready.

• You can enter for any one of three examination periods. These are shown below with their closing dates.

PERIOD	DURATION	CLOSING DATE
Period A	1st February to 15th March	1st December
Period B	1st May to 31st July	1st April
Period C	23rd October to 15th December	1st October

These dates will apply from 1st September 2006 until further notice

• Please complete the form giving the information required. Please fill in the type and level of exam, the instrument, along with the period and year. Finally, fill in the fee box with the appropriate amount. You can obtain up to date information on all Rockschool exam fees from the website: *www.rockschool.co.uk.* You should send this form with a cheque or postal order (payable to Rockschool Ltd) to the address shown on the order form. **Please also indicate on the form whether or not you would like to receive notification via email.**

• Applications received after the expiry of the closing date may be accepted subject to the payment of an additional fee.

• When you enter an exam you will receive from Rockschool an acknowledgement letter or email containing a copy of our exam regulations.

• Rockschool will allocate your entry to a centre and you will receive notification of the exam, showing a date, location and time as well as advice of what to bring to the centre. We endeavour to give you four weeks' notice of your exam.

• You should inform Rockschool of any cancellations or alterations to the schedule as soon as you can as it is usually not possible to transfer entries from one centre, or one period, to another without the payment of an additional fee.

• Please bring your music book and CD to the exam. You may not use photocopied music, nor the music used by someone else in another exam. The examiner will sign each book during each examination. You may be barred from taking an exam if you use someone else's music.

• You should aim to arrive for your Grade 6 exam thirty minutes before the time stated on the schedule.

• Each Grade 6 exam is scheduled to last for 30 minutes. You can use a small proportion of this time to tune up and get ready.

• Two to three weeks after the exam you will receive a copy of the examiner's mark sheet. Every successful player will receive a Rockschool certificate of achievement.